First SCIENCE Words

C O L O R I N G B O O K

The Ocean

Written by Q.L. Pearce
Illustrated by Christine Mallouf

Copyright ©1991 by RGA Publishing Group, Inc.
Published by Price Stern Sloan, Inc.
11150 Olympic Blvd., Suite 650, Los Angeles, CA 90064

ISBN: 0-8431-2912-3

10 9 8 7 6 5 4 3 2 1

PRICE STERN SLOAN

Los Angeles

Searching

Pelican

Snail

Fiddler crab

Can you find these other objects in the picture?

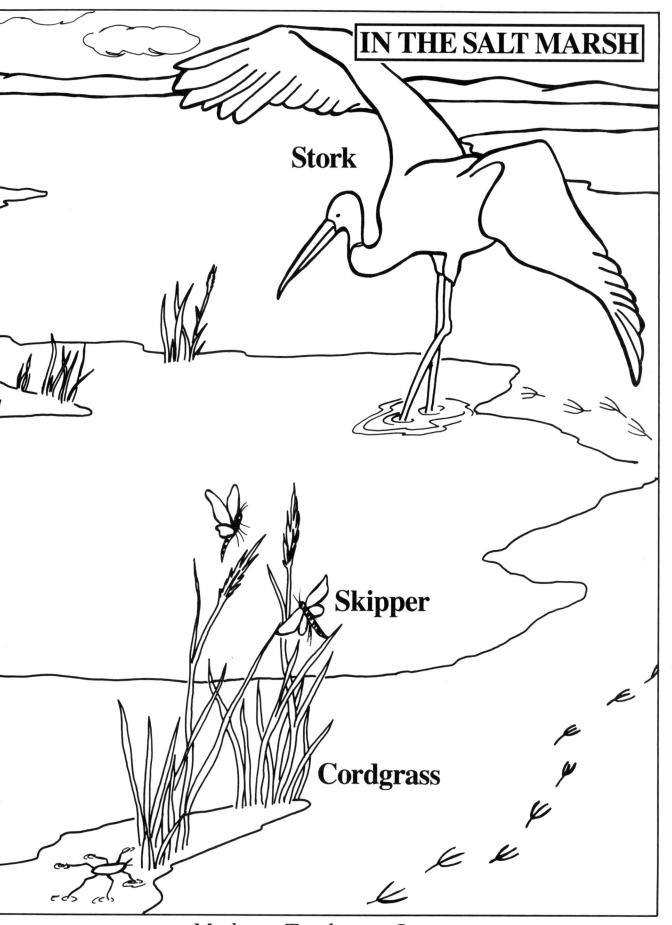

IN THE SALT MARSH

Stork

Skipper

Cordgrass

Mud   *Track*   *Leg*

Breaker

Terrace

Can you find these other objects in the picture?

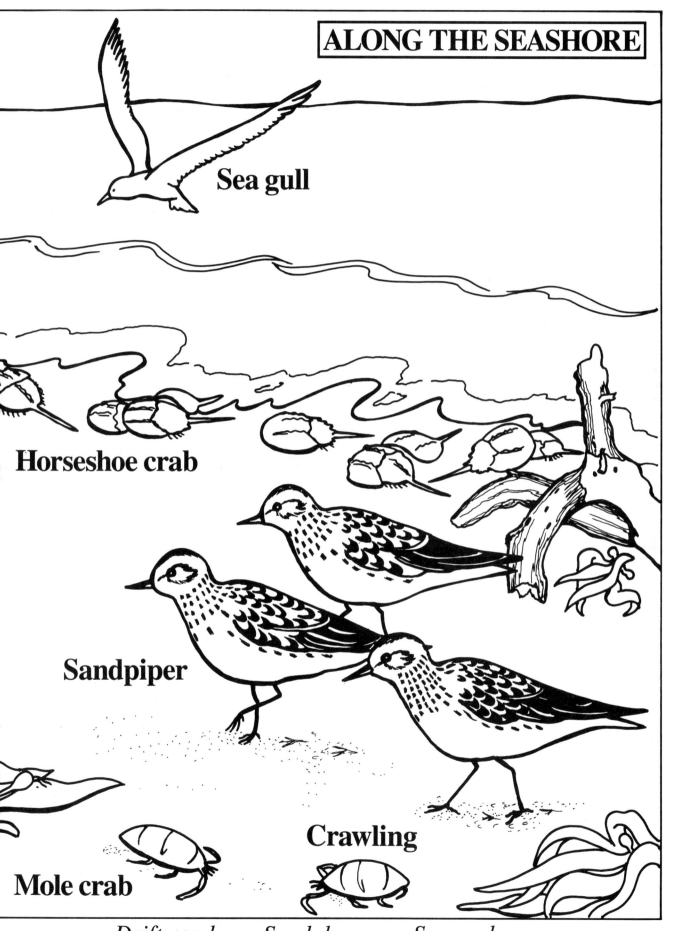

ALONG THE SEASHORE

Sea gull

Horseshoe crab

Sandpiper

Crawling

Mole crab

Driftwood   Sand dune   Seaweed

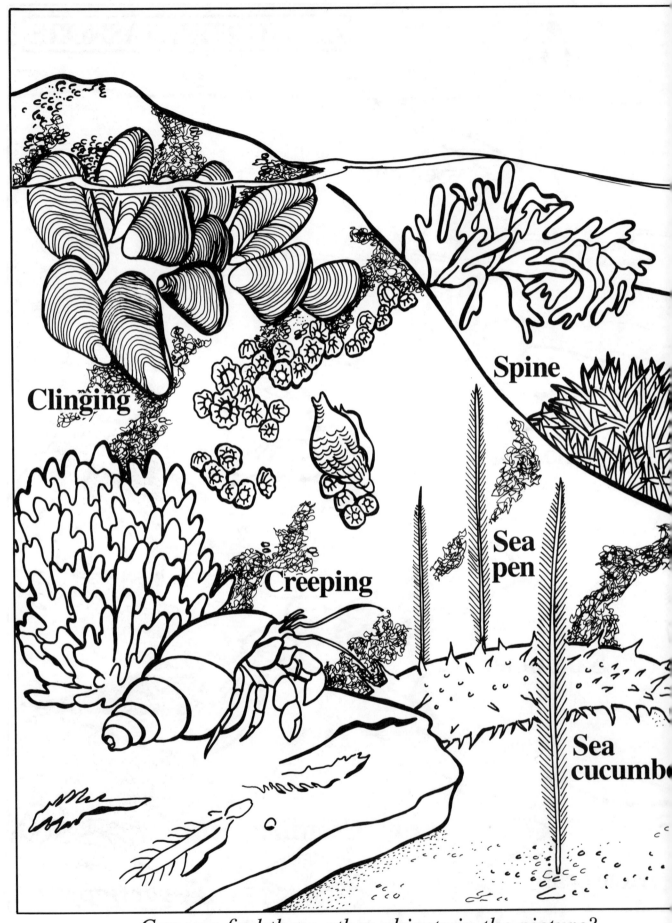

Clinging

Spine

Creeping

Sea pen

Sea cucumbe

Can you find these other objects in the picture?

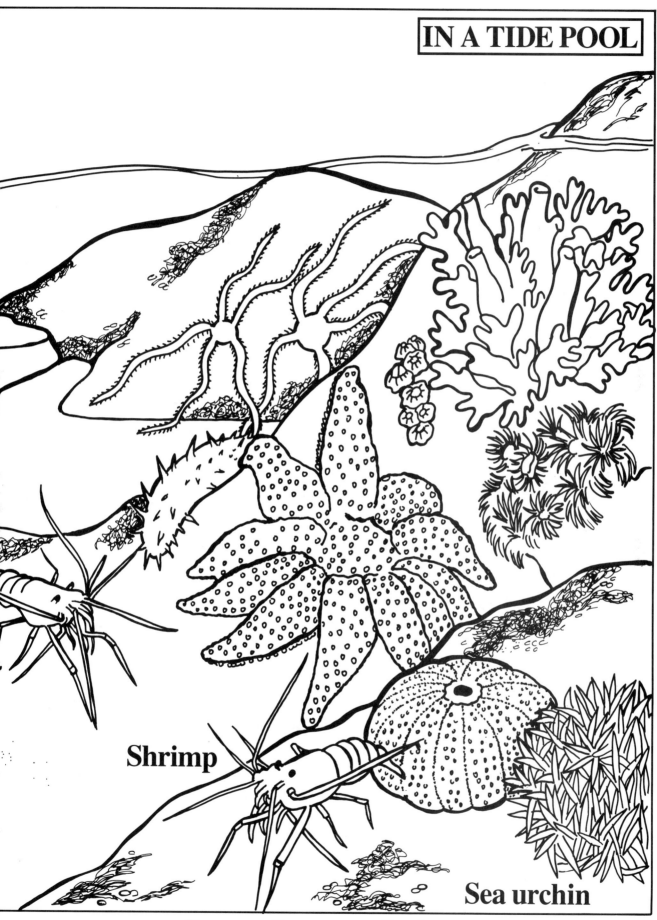

IN A TIDE POOL

Shrimp

Sea urchin

Eye   *Oyster*   *Rock*

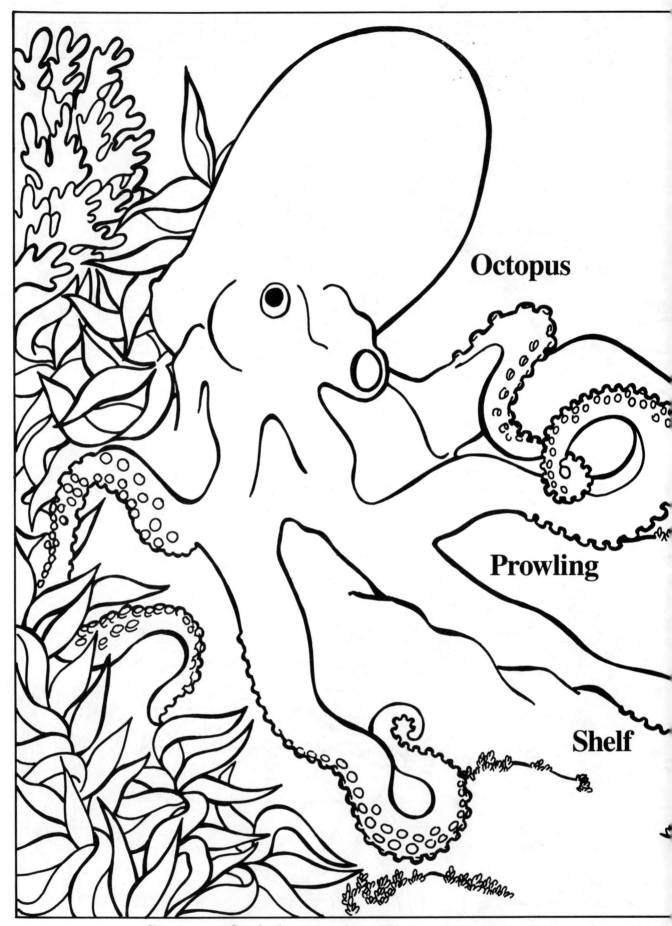

Octopus

Prowling

Shelf

Can you find these other objects in the picture?

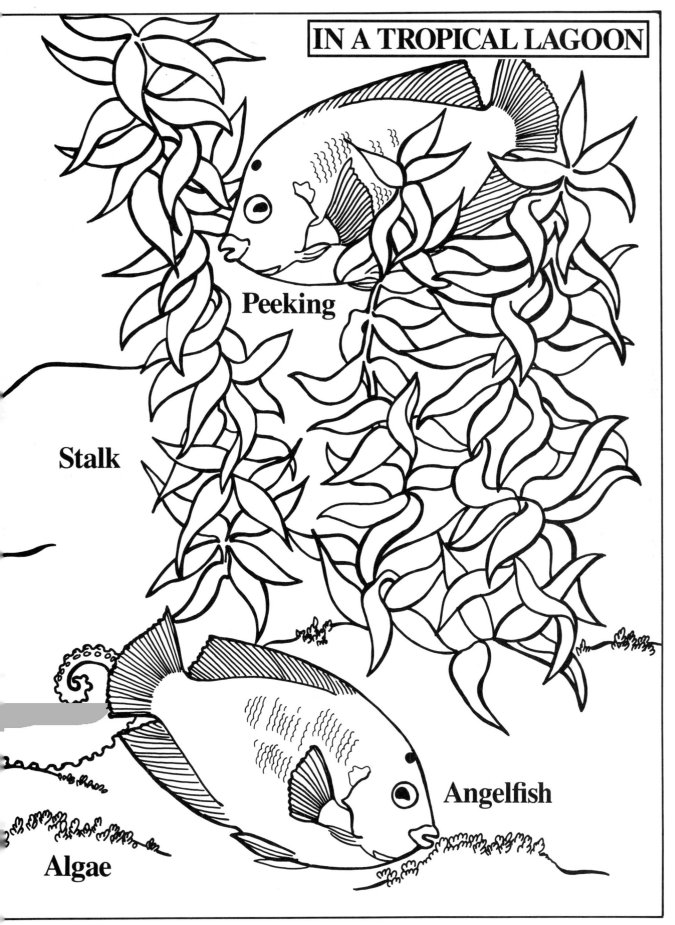

IN A TROPICAL LAGOON

Peeking

Stalk

Angelfish

Algae

Reef   Tentacle   Fin

Plume worm

Resting

Halibut

Sand dollar

Can you find these other objects in the picture?

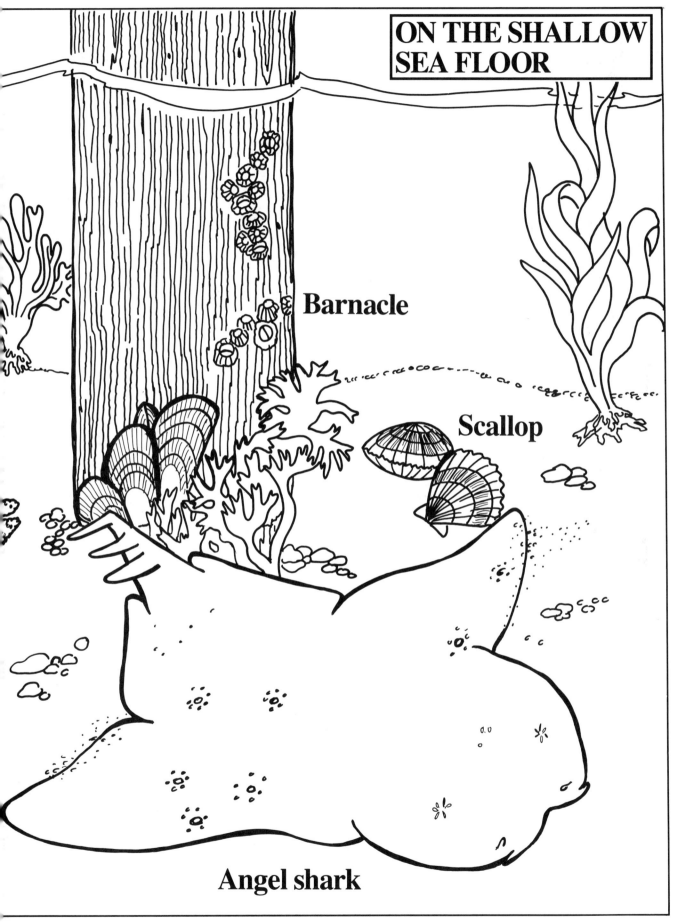

Barnacle

Scallop

Angel shark

Pebble   Sand   Stalk

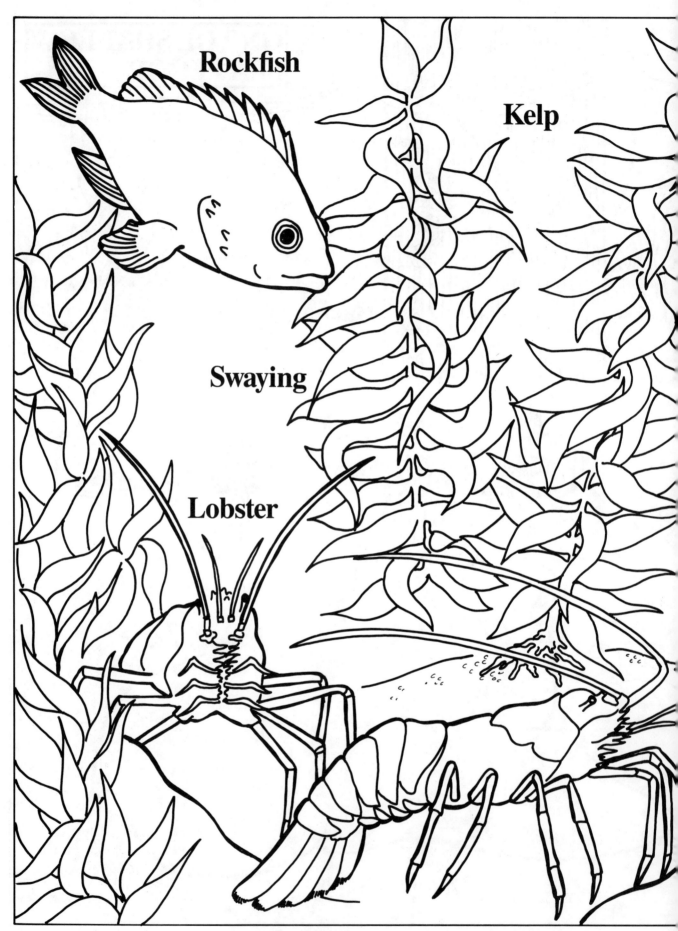

Can you find these other objects in the picture?

IN THE KELP FOREST

Sea lion

Hiding

Moray eel

Tooth   Nostril   Head

IN THE GREAT BARRIER REEF

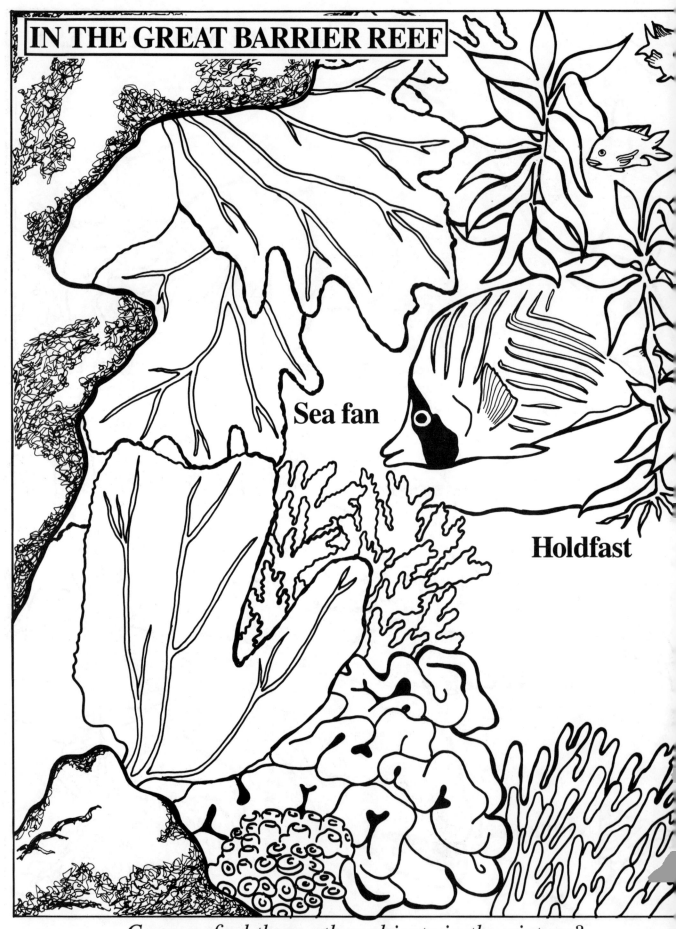

Sea fan

Holdfast

Can you find these other objects in the picture?

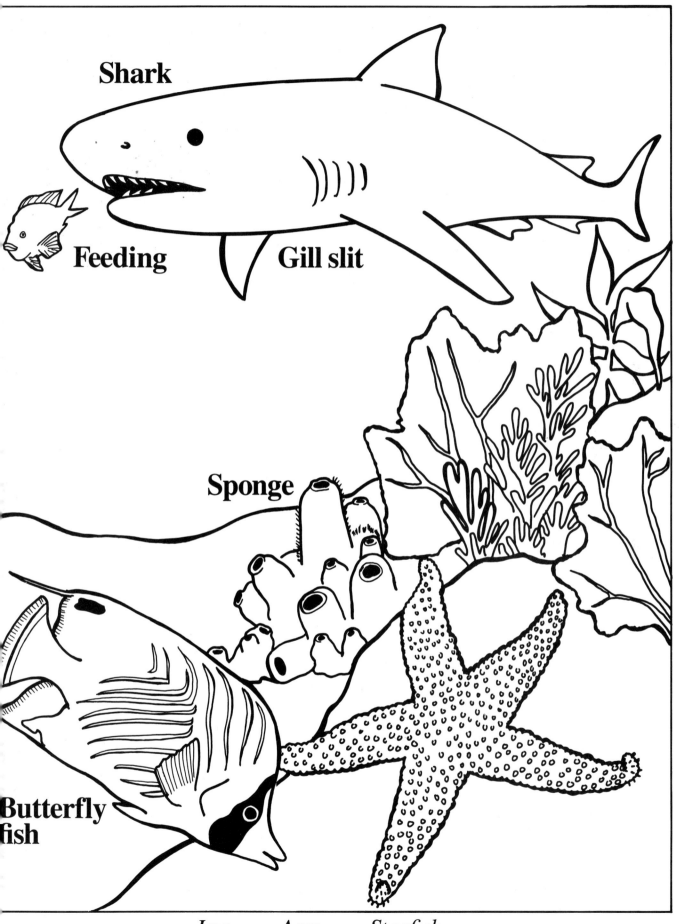

Shark

Feeding

Gill slit

Sponge

Butterfly fish

Jaw   *Arm*   *Starfish*

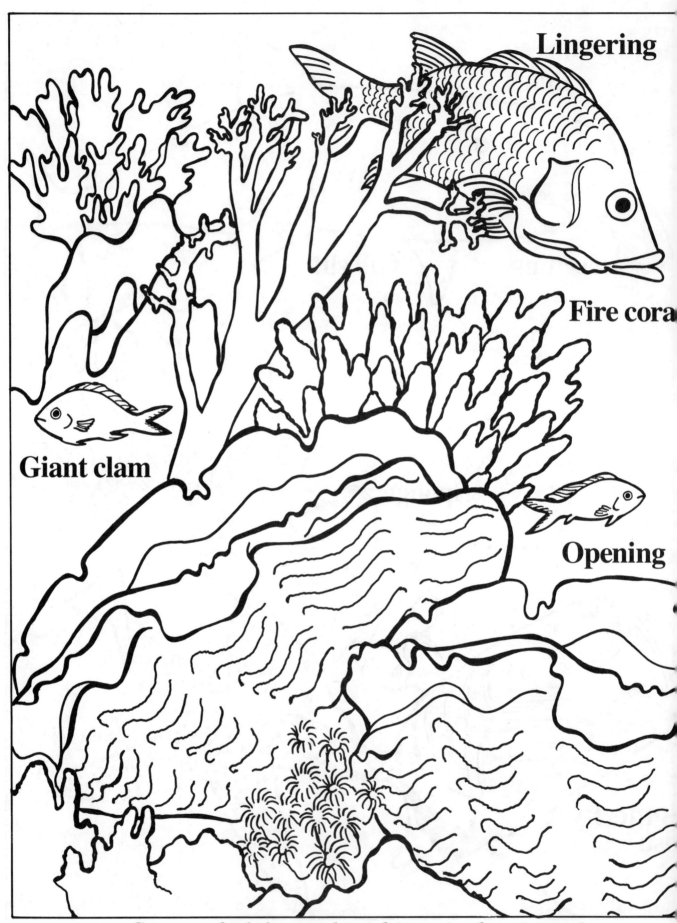

Lingering

Fire cora[l]

Opening

Giant clam

Can you find these other objects in the picture?

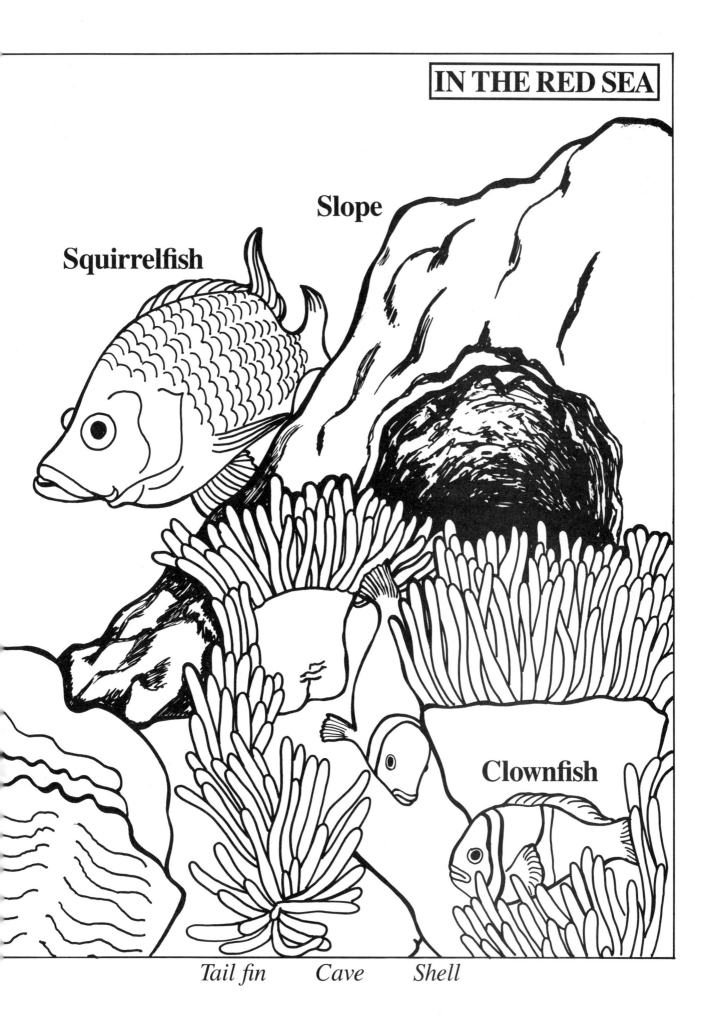

IN THE RED SEA

Slope

Squirrelfish

Clownfish

Tail fin   *Cave*   *Shell*

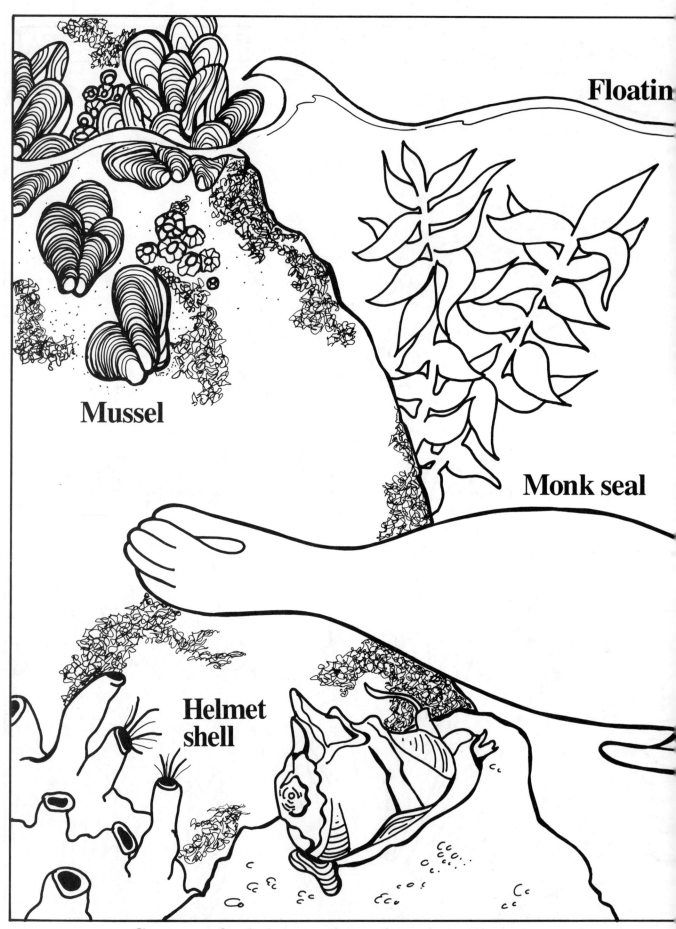

Floatin

Mussel

Monk seal

Helmet shell

Can you find these other objects in the picture?

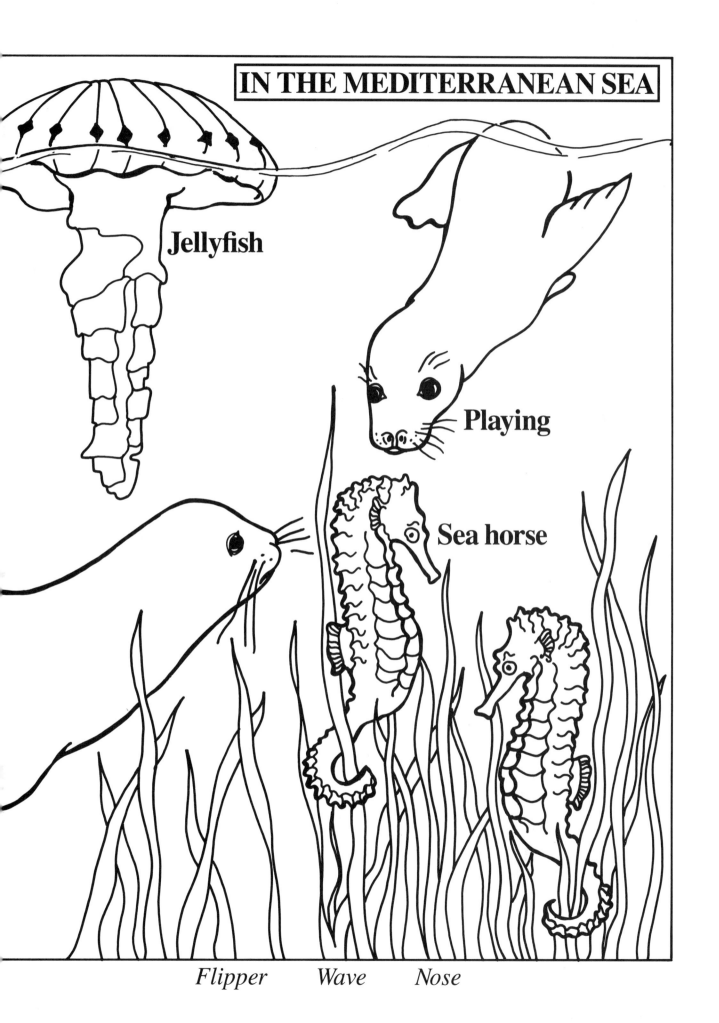

IN THE MEDITERRANEAN SEA

Jellyfish

Playing

Sea horse

Flipper   *Wave*   *Nose*

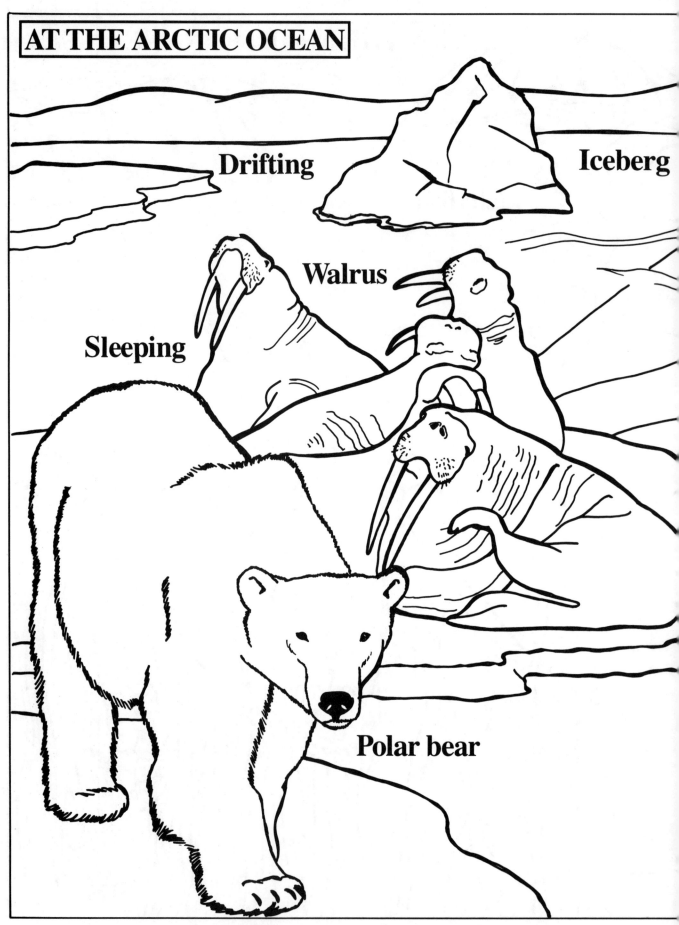

AT THE ARCTIC OCEAN

Drifting

Iceberg

Walrus

Sleeping

Polar bear

Can you find these other objects in the picture?

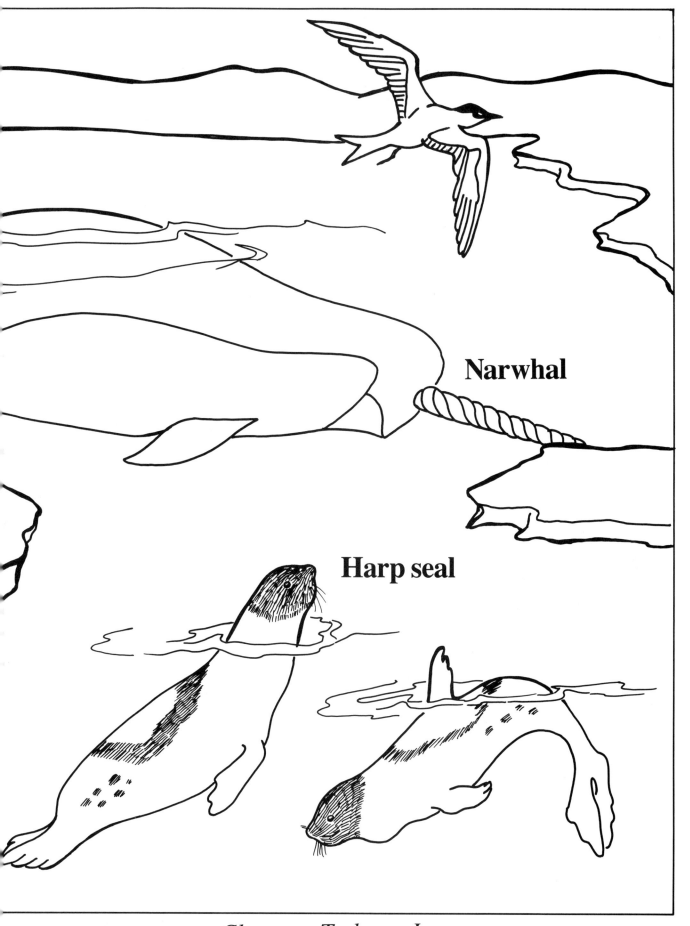

Narwhal

Harp seal

Claw   Tusk   Ice

IN ANTARCTIC WATERS

Killer whale

Penguin

Diving

Foot

Can you find these other objects in the picture?

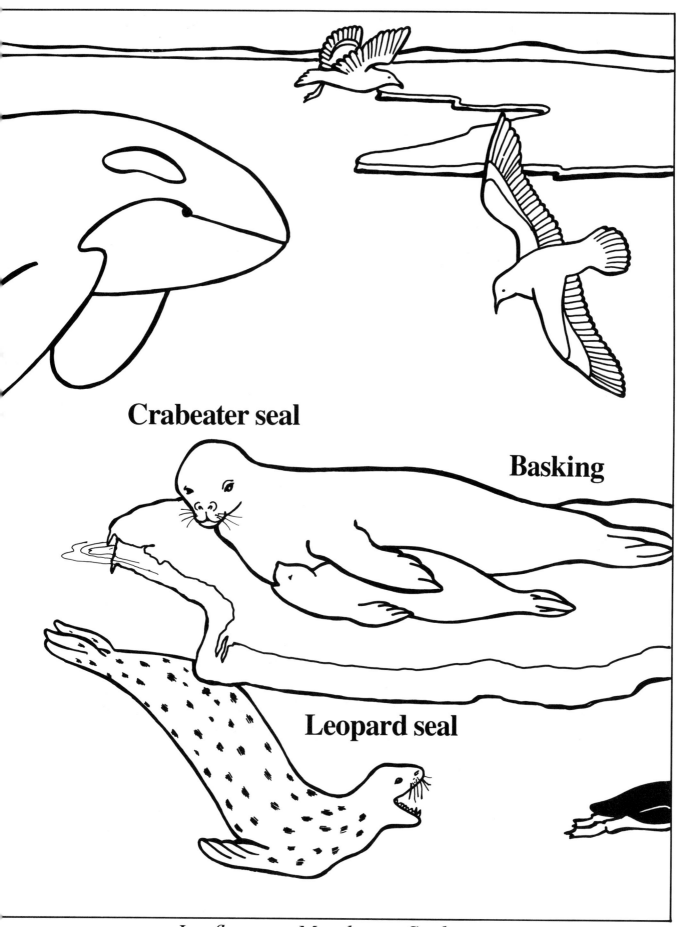

Crabeater seal

Basking

Leopard seal

Ice floe   *Mouth*   *Seal pup*

IN THE OPEN OCEAN

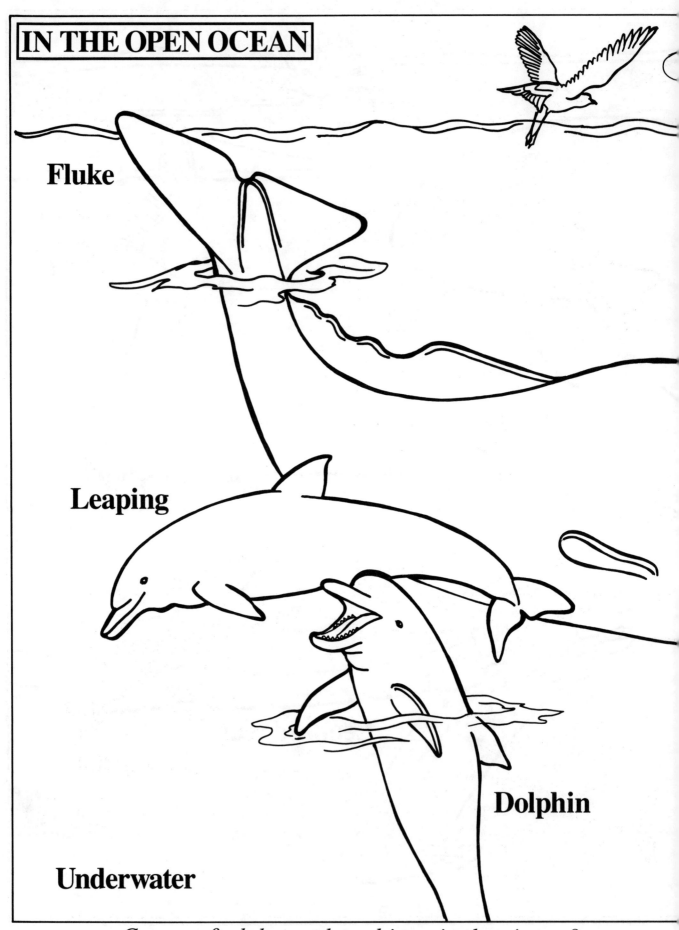

Fluke

Leaping

Dolphin

Underwater

Can you find these other objects in the picture?

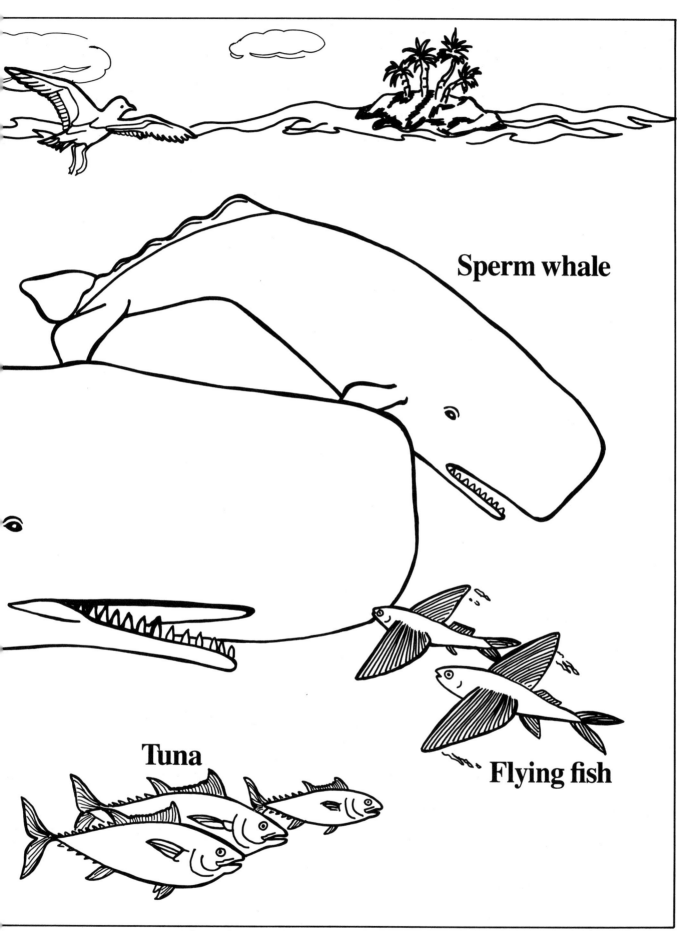

Sperm whale

Tuna

Flying fish

Island   Cloud   Whitecap

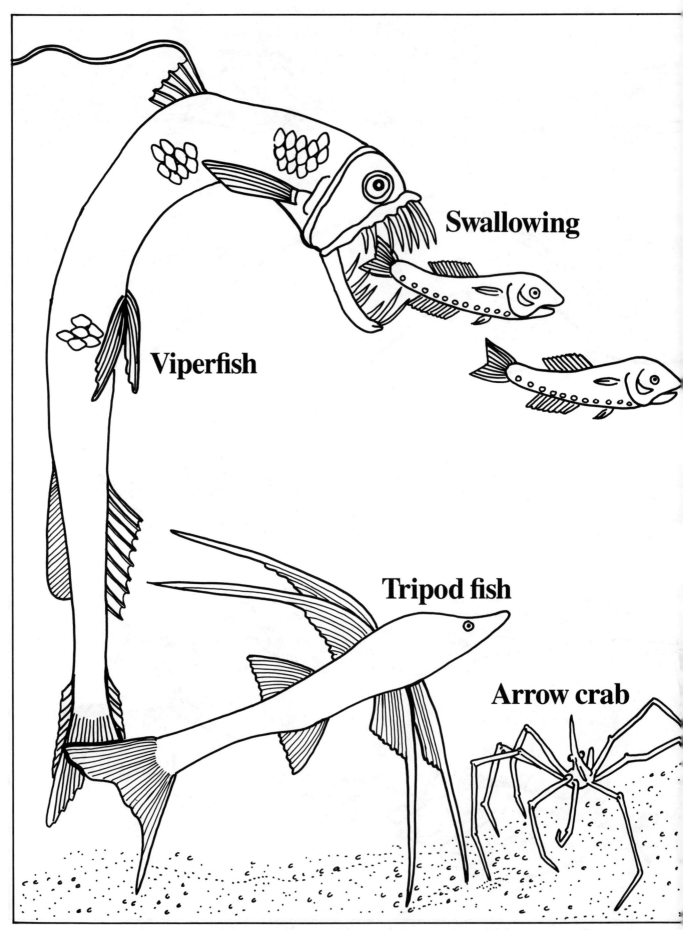

Swallowing

Viperfish

Tripod fish

Arrow crab

Can you find these other objects in the picture?

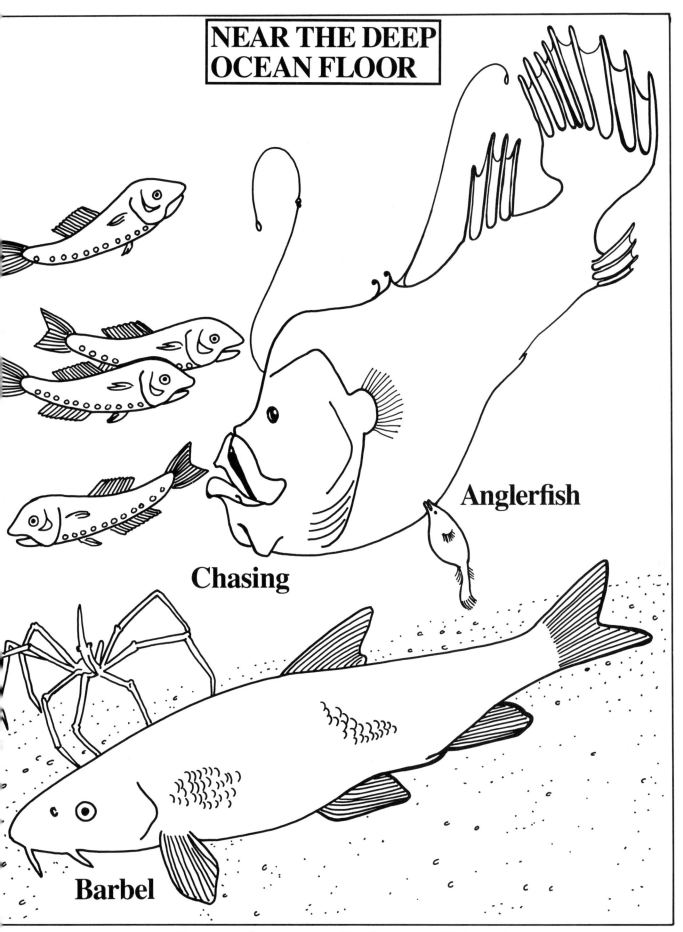

NEAR THE DEEP OCEAN FLOOR

Anglerfish

Chasing

Barbel

Ocean floor   *Body*   *Skin*

THE OCEAN

Can you name all the objects in the picture?

Turn the page to discover the answers.

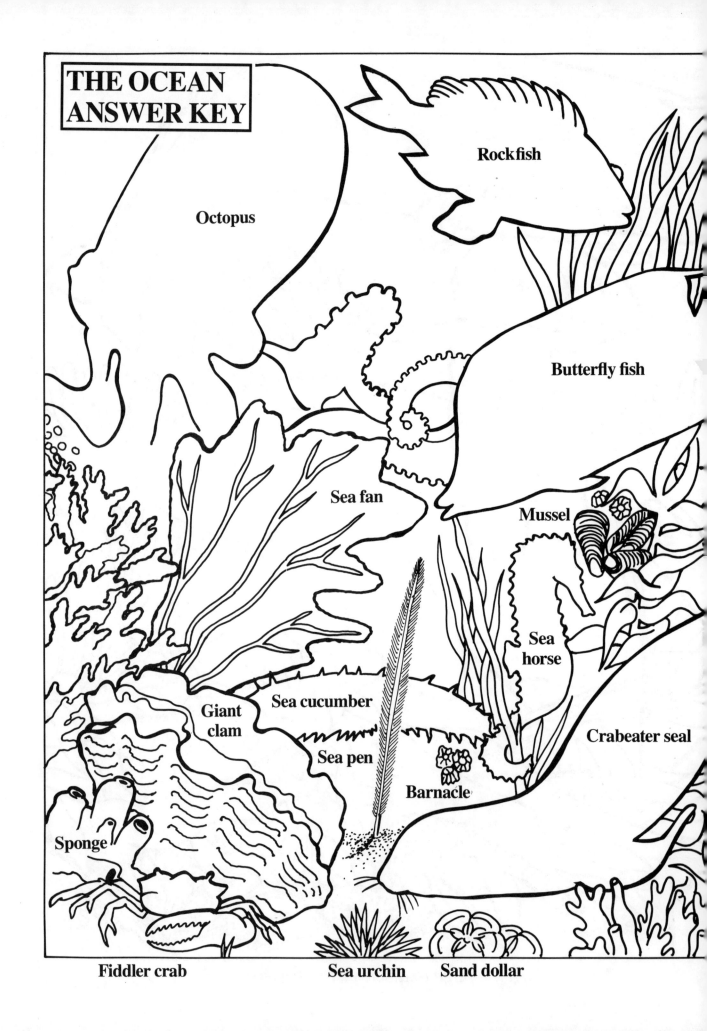

THE OCEAN ANSWER KEY

Octopus

Rockfish

Butterfly fish

Sea fan

Mussel

Sea horse

Giant clam

Sea cucumber

Sea pen

Crabeater seal

Barnacle

Sponge

Fiddler crab

Sea urchin

Sand dollar

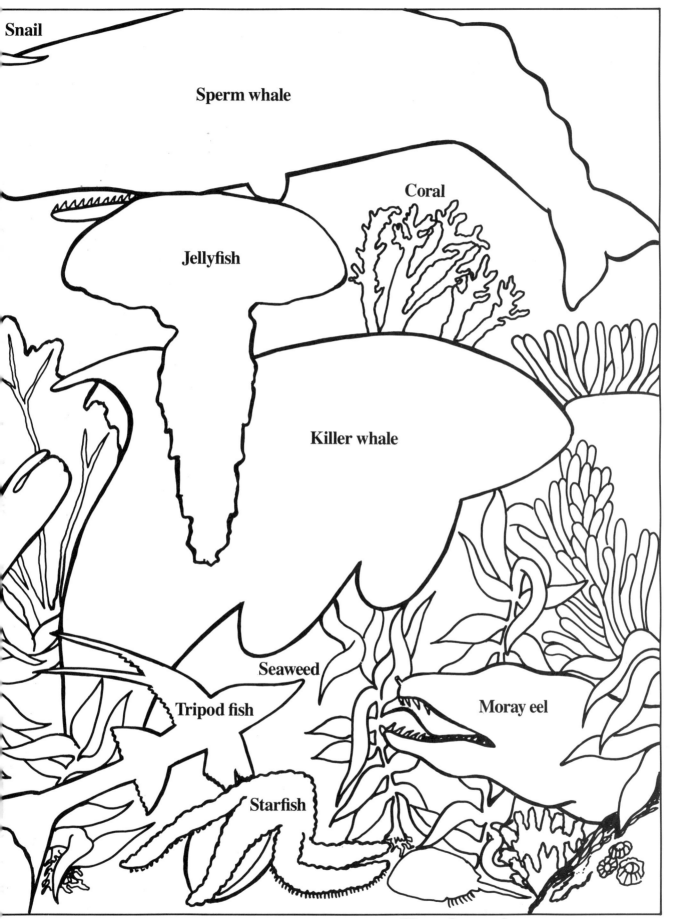

Snail

Sperm whale

Coral

Jellyfish

Killer whale

Seaweed

Tripod fish

Moray eel

Starfish

Horseshoe crab

Here are the names of objects you have learned about. Can you remember what each looks like?

IN THE SALT MARSH

Fiddler crab   Skipper   Snail   Cordgrass

Stork   Searching   Pelican

ALONG THE SEASHORE

Sandpiper   Breaker   Mole crab   Terrace

Horseshoe crab   Crawling   Sea gull

IN A TIDE POOL

Spine   Shrimp   Sea pen   Clinging

Sea cucumber   Creeping   Sea urchin

IN A TROPICAL LAGOON

Algae   Shelf   Stalk   Octopus

Prowling   Angelfish   Peeking

ON THE SHALLOW SEA FLOOR

Halibut   Angel shark   Resting   Scallop

Plume worm   Sand dollar   Barnacle

IN THE KELP FOREST

Rockfish   Hiding   Kelp   Swaying

Moray eel   Sea lion   Lobster

IN THE GREAT BARRIER REEF

Shark   Feeding   Gill slit   Sponge

Butterfly fish   Sea fan   Holdfast

IN THE RED SEA

Fire coral   Slope   Clownfish   Lingering

Squirrelfish   Giant clam   Opening

IN THE MEDITERRANEAN SEA

Mussel   Jellyfish   Floating   Helmet shell

Sea horse   Monk seal   Playing

AT THE ARCTIC OCEAN

Narwhal   Harp seal   Iceberg   Driftin

Polar bear   Sleeping   Walrus

IN ANTARCTIC WATERS

Foot   Killer whale   Penguin   Diving

Leopard seal   Crabeater seal   Basking

IN THE OPEN OCEAN

Fluke   Tuna   Dolphin   Leaping

Flying fish   Sperm whale   Underwater

NEAR THE DEEP OCEAN FLOOR

Viperfish   Chasing   Anglerfish   Swallowing

Barbel   Tripod fish   Arrow crab